Weight Training

for the martial artist

Geoff Thompson

SUMMERSDALE

Summersdale Publishers Ltd
46 West Street
Chichester
West Sussex
PO19 1RP
United Kingdom

www.summersdale.com

Printed and bound in Great Britain.

ISBN 1 84024 183 7

First edit by Kerry Thompson.

Photographs by David W. Monks, member of the Master Photographers' Association
Snappy Snaps Portrait Studio
7 Cross Cheaping
Coventry
CV1 1HF

Important note

If you have or believe you may have a medical condition the techniques outlined in this book should not be attempted without first consulting your doctor. Some of the techniques in this book require a high level of fitness and suppleness and should not be attempted by someone lacking such fitness. The author and the publishers cannot accept any responsibility for any proceedings or prosecutions brought or instituted against any person or body as a result of the use or misuse of any techniques described in this book or any loss, injury or damage caused thereby.

About the author

Geoff Thompson has written over 20 books and is known worldwide for his bestselling autobiography, *Watch My Back*, about his nine years working as a nightclub doorman. He currently has a quarter of a million books in print. He holds the rank of 6th Dan black belt in Japanese karate, 1st Dan in judo and is also qualified to senior instructor level in various other forms of wrestling and martial arts. He has several scripts for stage and screen in development with Destiny Films.

He has published articles for *GQ* magazine, and has also been featured in *FHM*, *Maxim*, *Arena*, *Front* and *Loaded* magazines, and has appeared many times on mainstream television.

Geoff is currently a contributing editor for *Men's Fitness* magazine.

For a free colour brochure of Geoff Thompson's
books and videos please ring the
24-hour hotline on 02476 431100 or write to:

Geoff Thompson Ltd
PO Box 307
Coventry
CV3 2YP

www.geoffthompson.com
www.summersdale.com

For my beautiful wife Sharon.

CONTENTS

INTRODUCTION
BY DAVE TURTON
SENIOR NABA COACH

Dave has been a NABA (National Amateur Bodybuilding Association) life member since 1964, an area judge since 1974 and the official stage manager for the Mr Universe, Mr Britain, Mr Scotland and Mr North-West Britain bodybuilding championships. He is a senior instructor in weight training for NABA and has trained with former Mr Britains and a former Mr Universe. Dave Turton is also a 5th Dan black belt in Goshin Kai ju-jitsu.

Before Geoff goes into listing the best exercises and routines for the use of weight training for the martial artist, it is advisable to explain more of what weight training is, and, more to the point, what it should be.

There is a long history of the multitude of different systems of personal combat, full of examples of the use of progressive resistance exercises to improve an individual's own abilities. Therefore it would be superfluous to list the history of 'weight training' in the combat arts, and more beneficial to try to understand how best to use it both for you and your art.

Firstly, weight training is to be viewed in the same context as running or stretching. That is as a supplementary aid to the combat skills, not as a replacement for them. Weight training is used to improve the strength of a weaker trainee and to give work to the muscles pertaining to your art. After all, if you had been a bodybuilder and power-lifter to competition standards since your sixteenth birthday, and now at 26 years old, six-foot tall and fifteen stone and are just starting karate, your power development wouldn't be a worry.

What weight training is not:

In the early days when sportsmen and athletes were trying out the weights in order to become better at their chosen event, a few mistakes were made. Most sportsmen with no knowledge of how to train with the weights turned to the weight-lifting and bodybuilding fraternity for help and advice. Unfortunately very few knew how to use the weights to improve other athletes' performances. Weight-lifting, bodybuilding and power-lifting are separate athletic sciences which happen to use the same tools, but in totally different ways (not everyone in a tracksuit and trainers is a sprinter, a miler or a decathlete). After all, would you ask a soccer coach to train a rugger team simply because both sports use a field, a ball and two teams?

So, the well-meaning bodybuilders put the other sportsmen on bodybuilding routines, and the hoped for results didn't materialise.

Bodybuilding is about developing the many muscle groups so that, along with a loss of fat, the shape, balance and development are at the optimum levels. It is important to a competitive bodybuilder to ensure correct and balanced development of all muscles and muscle groups. Intercostals, serratus and brachialis need work but a karataka shouldn't be too concerned about minor muscles, more about improved functions.

So, weight training isn't bodybuilding, nor power-lifting nor weight-lifting.

What is weight training?

Weight training is the use of progressive resistance training to improve the power output, function and strength of an athlete. It strengthens weaker muscle groups, and aids in using the increase in strength and power to improve your sport. Seen in this way we can now look more at how useful weight training can be.

There are two further divisions and subdivisions in the understanding of this subject. Firstly, the art that you are in, secondly, your personal needs. Taken in context, the needs of judo, karate, kendo, tai-chi, sumo, kyudo and wing-chun, are all different; likewise, the needs of a 16-year-old girl in aikido will naturally differ from those of a 26-year-old, sixteen-stone judo international.

People differ, so their needs for weight training also vary. Arts differ; punching and kicking arts have different needs to the pulling, lifting and throwing arts. Admittedly, these are generalisations, but they are quite valid.

So now we can look at the exercises and the ways that we can use them to improve our chosen arts.

Weight Training for the Martial Artist

For the purposes of martial arts improvement, we will first look at the muscle groups most used, the 'best' exercises, sets and reps (repetitions), and some exercises that you shouldn't use.

There will be two basic routines, one more useful for the punching and kicking arts, such as karate, tae-kwondo and Chinese 'hard' systems; the other for the holding and throwing systems like aikido, judo, some of the ju-jitsu systems and wrestling.

Two further pieces of advice:

1) As your other training (running, stretching, etc.) will work the endurance factors of your overall fitness, then weights should be used for fairly low repetitions (in the 6-12 range) to balance out the fast and slow twitch fibres.

2) All the body should be worked; there should be no weaknesses. Having said that, extra emphasis should be placed on the muscle groups that are most used in your art.

As far as the type of training goes, I have preferences for the use of weights. I shall list my do's and don'ts, with appropriate explanatory comments when needed (don't worry, we'll get to the nitty-gritty eventually – but the more that you know about and understand a subject, the better for you).

Firstly, forget the many machines: basic bar-bells and dumb-bells, bench and squat racks are enough. Many machines make your muscles work in fixed 'grooves'; with free weights, you find the balance and adjust with secondary muscles.

Secondly, where feasible, use dumb-bells in preference to bar-bells. The reasoning here is that a bar 'fixes' the hands in a set position (which never occurs in a combat situation), and also a balanced bar doesn't allow for that little extra work and coordination for the weaker side.

Thirdly, train muscle groups and not just individual muscles. Nowhere in a combat scenario would *any* muscle work totally independent to others. For example, seated concentration dumb-bell curls are great for the bodybuilder who desires that extra 'peak' on his biceps, but it is of no use to a judoka trying to lift a sixteen-stone opponent.

Enough said, enjoy the book, learn from it, and make weight training an integral part of your martial arts' training.

PREFACE

This book is less about developing physical strength and more about building a sinewy armour. It is not meant as a tool to make you a physical leviathan, rather it is about using iron to mould your character and enhance your martial art. Physical strength, per se, is of little use in self-defence if it is not backed by a steely resolve and good physical technique. So please don't look upon this text as a 'get big quick' manual for those with a sagging esteem. Weight training (in this context) is merely an addition to your martial art. Fights are not won at a high level with strength; they are won with cunning and sharp technique. A small man with good technique and a strong intention will take a big man with no technique out of the game before he even realises he is in it.

On the door, as a bouncer, I was subject to many unsolicited attacks where quickness to the punch and good technique meant the difference between winning and ending up in a hospital bed. So the old argument that training with the iron slows you down is unfounded. The weights never once impeded my ability to be first; I never woke up with a crowd around me once in my nine years. I always made it my job to be first, and if I thought for one second that weight training was going to subtract from that in any way I'd drop its use like a hot brick.

This is not meant as a comprehensive text on weight training. There are many methods and theories when it comes to training with weights, and this is just one of them. Weight training is a very subjective business and I am not in the game of trying to put anyone – or their system – down, but this is one of the ways I train with the weights. It has worked for me and countless others and hopefully it will work for you.

There is one word that rises again and again in what I practice: that word is REAL.

Is what I am practising real?

Will it help me to achieve my ultimate goal?

If the answer to either or both is 'no', I don't use it. After nine years of having lived with violence and the violent I have developed a bullshit detector that allows me to smell shit from a thousand yards away. I just know when something is of no use.

Weight Training for the Martial Artist

Training with the weights is a means to an end, with me anyway, rather than an end in itself. My aim is not to develop a beach physique, though as a by-product that might be nice, nor to be able to lift heavy weights just so that I can say 'I can lift heavy weights'. My aim is not to get massive in the false belief that 'big is hard', because it isn't. My aim was, and still is, to train with weights progressively to aid me in my budo.

A by-product of training with the weights is that it helps to develop confidence and esteem: if you look good, you feel good, but confidence is of little use without the back-up artillery. If there is no back-up artillery, as in a good combat system, confidence is just a sugar pedestal that will crumble as soon as the rain comes in.

I have loved doing weights for the past thirty odd years and love it still today. It has enabled me to back up good technique with quality muscle and the same muscle mass has also enabled me to take it when the going got a little tough. I sincerely believe that training with weights will enhance any system and give added confidence to its exponents.

Also worthy of a mention is the fact that, with the use of weights and a good diet, I have managed to put on five stone of good quality bodyweight over the last years. It might be that you are happy with the bodyweight that you carry, you may even want to lose weight. The beauty of training with weights is it allows for all this: if you want to gain weight, maintain weight or lose weight you can, the option is there for you, though of course diet is the bigger part of this computation.

CHAPTER ONE:
A LOOK AT THE EQUIPMENT

When writing a book of this genre, one cannot just assume knowledge, so this chapter is to show the reader the working tools of weight training. For those that already know what the equipment is and how it works, feel free to move on to the next chapter.

As Dave said in the introduction, free weights are preferable to machine weights for the stated reasons. So I won't list the myriad machines that may be found in the gyms around the country. This is not to say that machine training is not sound, it surely is, but you can't beat free weights.

Dumb-bells

These are used to work all aspects of the torso (and occasionally the legs). Used in a curling, pushing, pressing, and lifting manner. They are held in each hand and used alternately or together. They are comprised of a short metal bar to which free weights are attached to each end; the weight is secured with 'collars' that stop the free weight from slipping off the bar during exercise. (Pic 1)

Loose Weight

Cast-iron or vinyl discs that come in different sizes. Different weights are used to add weight to dumb-bells or bar-bells. (Pic 2)

Bar-bells

The bar-bell is a steel bar which varies in size, usually from 1.2m (4ft) to 2.1m (7ft) long. Loose weight is added to each end of the bar in equal proportions and sealed with collars to stop the weight falling off during exercise.

(Pic 3)

Triceps Bar

This is a special bar used for training the triceps (back upper arms). When working the triceps in the forthcoming routines it is an option for the trainee to use this piece of equipment or the ordinary straight bar. (Pic 4)

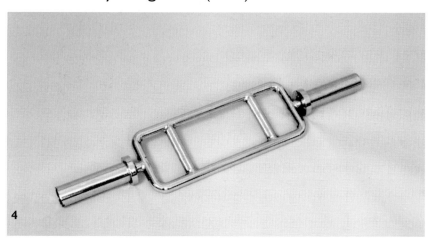

4

Curl Bar

The curl bar is another specialised bar that helps to isolate and/or strengthen the biceps (front upper arm) and triceps (back upper arm). (Pic 5)

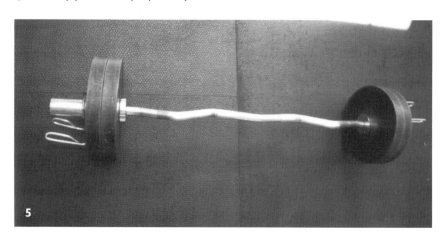

5

Flat Bench

This is used for sitting or lying exercises involving dumb-bell and bar-bell training. The flat bench enables the trainee to work the major part of the muscle group; the shoulders and chest. (Pic 6)

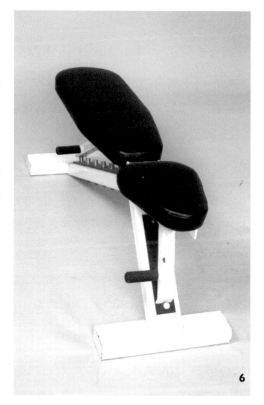

Incline/Decline Bench

The incline/decline bench is used for sitting or lying exercises involving dumb-bell and bar-bell exercises. The incline/decline bench enables the trainee to work different parts of the major muscle group, i.e. upper or lower chest, front shoulders. (Pic 7)

23

Gloves

Fingerless gloves can help protect the hands when lifting weights. (Pic 8)

Belt

A waist belt is a good protection from back strain when lifting weights.

Clothing

Training clothes need to be comfortable and either baggy or Lycra stretch. During training the muscles expand and can be very uncomfortable if training clothes are tight or restrictive.

Baggy tracksuits, one-piece leotards and tights that stretch (for women); loose-fitting cotton T-shirts or vests and loose shorts (for men) are all ideal for comfortable training.

I always find it a good idea to take a towel, soap, shampoo and a change of clothing for after training. This is preferable to going home in sweaty gear. A towel is also very handy for taking into the gym with you for mopping the brow.

CHAPTER TWO
A LOOK AT THE BODY

Whilst we are mostly concerned here with strength training, it is also worth mentioning that a degree of cardiovascular training (involving the heart and lungs) must go hand in hand with progressive resistance training for overall success. This is because muscles are supplied with energy by the heart and lungs, which in turn increase the blood circulation and breathing to enable exercise to continue. If the heart and lungs are not also trained they cannot keep up with the muscles' demand; fatigue soon sets in and the muscles stop functioning.

The stiffness experienced in the muscles after training is due to a waste product (lactic acid) staying in the muscle. This can be prevented by 'warming down' after training or by further exercise.

WHAT IS MUSCLE?

There are three kinds of muscle in the body, each holding its very own characteristics. I shall list them in order:

1) Smooth Muscle

This is found in the walls of internal or visceral organs; blood vessels and intestines for instance.

2) Cardiac Muscle

This is the tissue that makes up the heart. It can be strengthened by cardiovascular or high repetition exercises such as running, swimming and cycling.

3) Skeletal Muscle

This is a system of long muscles that control the movement of the body. These are the very muscles that we, as weight trainers, aim to strengthen and condition.

THE FUNCTION OF MUSCLE

Muscle has one and only one function: it contracts. This is why our bodies are designed with opposing muscles and groups of muscles. When one part of the body is extended in one direction it takes the contraction of an opposing muscle to bring it back. For instance, the triceps at the back of the upper arm will help to push the arm out in the execution of a punch, whilst the biceps at the front of the upper arm will help bring the arm back on retraction of the punch.

Muscles tend to work to demand; if you place added stress upon them they will expand to meet that stress. If there is no stress placed upon them, for instance when your arm is in a sling for a couple of months, the muscle will deteriorate and shrink. This is why a road digger will naturally develop muscles that a clerk might not. Weight training is a controlled way of placing extra stress on muscles or muscle groups to develop extra size and strength.

The shrinking of muscle due to under use is called atrophy, whilst the increase in size and strength when muscle is subjected to greater amounts of stress is called hypertrophy.

Weight Training for the Martial Artist

I know that there will be cynics out there saying that your own art will develop the muscles that it needs for use within that art. This is not necessarily true: exercises like callisthenics, running, swimming and the kind of repetition that we do in martial arts to develop technique are of the fixed resistance kind, so no matter how long you do them, you are always contracting the muscles against the same resistance. You may, with this type of practice, learn to do a given exercise or technique for longer periods of time, which means that your endurance has improved, but you will not necessarily get any stronger, no matter how many reps you do.

If you want to keep getting stronger, you have to keep increasing the resistance; that way the muscles have to continue to adapt. The beauty of progressive resistance training is that it never gets easy; every time you feel like it is getting too easy you just add a little more weight to your bar or dumb-bell and the exercise becomes difficult again and the muscles adapt and develop to the new demands placed upon them.

FRONT VIEW

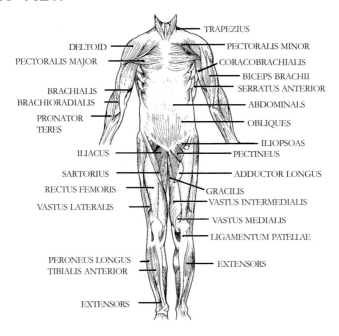

DELTOID
PECTORALIS MAJOR
BRACHIALIS
BRACHIORADIALIS
PRONATOR TERES
ILIACUS
SARTORIUS
RECTUS FEMORIS
VASTUS LATERALIS
PERONEUS LONGUS
TIBIALIS ANTERIOR
EXTENSORS

TRAPEZIUS
PECTORALIS MINOR
CORACOBRACHIALIS
BICEPS BRACHII
SERRATUS ANTERIOR
ABDOMINALS
OBLIQUES
ILIOPSOAS
PECTINEUS
ADDUCTOR LONGUS
GRACILIS
VASTUS INTERMEDIALIS
VASTUS MEDIALIS
LIGAMENTUM PATELLAE
EXTENSORS

REAR VIEW

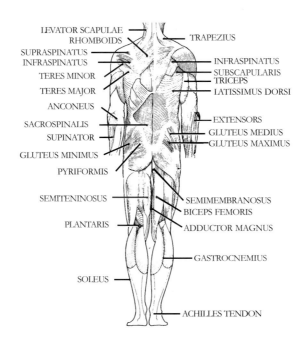

LEVATOR SCAPULAE
RHOMBOIDS
SUPRASPINATUS
INFRASPINATUS
TERES MINOR
TERES MAJOR
ANCONEUS
SACROSPINALIS
SUPINATOR
GLUTEUS MINIMUS
PYRIFORMIS
SEMITENINOSUS
PLANTARIS
SOLEUS

TRAPEZIUS
INFRASPINATUS
SUBSCAPULARIS
TRICEPS
LATISSIMUS DORSI
EXTENSORS
GLUTEUS MEDIUS
GLUTEUS MAXIMUS
SEMIMEMBRANOSUS
BICEPS FEMORIS
ADDUCTOR MAGNUS
GASTROCNEMIUS
ACHILLES TENDON

There are over six hundred working muscles in the body, some of which are listed above, but we are really only concerned with the major muscles in the body, and more specifically the ones that are used in the execution of our art.

I will start from the neck and work my way down the body listing the main function of the muscle.

LEVATOR SCAPULAE MUSCLE (NECK)

The neck's function is to rotate, turn and support the head. Neck strengthening is very important because injuries to this small muscle can impede everything that we do. It's hard to throw a punch if the neck is injured and multidirectional training is also badly impeded.

TRAPEZIUS MUSCLES

The trapezius muscles aid in pulling and shrugging movements and, if trained, are very powerful muscles. They are situated in the major upper back and get their name because of their trapezium shape.

DELTOID MUSCLES (SHOULDER)

The deltoid, or shoulder, muscles consist of three heads that rotate and lift the arms to the front side and back, and also tie into the pectoral (chest) muscle at the front of the torso and assist in any movements concerning the chest. The deltoids are used especially in movements that require push or punch from the front or above the head.

TRICEPS
(UPPER BACK ARM)

The triceps cover the whole of the back of the upper arm and extend right down to the elbow. They actually take up two-thirds of the upper arm and greatly assist in any pushing or punching motion, especially where the hands are too close together to use the chest and shoulder muscles.

BICEPS
(FRONT UPPER ARM)

Quite a small muscle at the higher upper arm that assists in retracting the arm from an extended position and assists in hugging motions.

FLEXORS AND EXTENSORS
(FOREARM)

These muscles control the wrists and the fingers, aiding a strong grip.

LATISSIMUS DORSI (LOWER BACK)

The lats are very powerful back muscles used in any endeavour involved in pulling the elbows inwards, pulling the body upwards or hugging.

ERECTORS

These are situated under the pectoral muscle and are primarily used to help in the upward movement of the upper body and back.

PECTORALS
(CHEST)

These connect the chest to the upper arm and shoulder. The major and minor parts of the muscle help pull arms inwards (hugging) and push weight outwards.

ABDOMINALS
(STOMACH)

The powerful stomach comprises of eight muscles, all attached together in a complex manner. They help support the upper body and move the body inwards. They are also pivotal in helping the body up from a reclined, inclined or declined position.

OBLIQUES
(SIDE STOMACH)

The obliques help to bend and twist the body and assist the front stomach in rising from a reclined position.

QUADRICEPS
(THIGH MUSCLES)

These are large and powerful leg muscles that extend across the front of the thighs. Used primarily to extend the thighs. Pivotal in squatting motions.

GLUTIUS MAXIMUS
(BUTTOCKS)

The glutes help to lift the legs in a backwards motion and assist in squatting motions (when trained they look good too).

GASTROCNEMIUS
(CALVES, BACK LOWER LEGS)

The calves help to raise the body onto the toes.

ANTERIOR MUSCLES
(FRONT OF THE LOWER LEG)

All the movements of the ankles and toes are controlled by these muscles.

CHAPTER THREE
A LOOK AT YOUR ART

This book is not about what your art is or is not, neither is it about whether or not your art is effective. That would be out of the context of a book on weight training. For more detail on the effectiveness of various combative arts please refer to my other texts, more specifically *Animal Day – Pressure Testing the Martial Arts*.

First and foremost, let's keep things in context: weight training is an addition to your combat art, it is not a substitute, nor is it the missing link in an art that might be lacking when it comes to adapting to a street situation. So let me state categorically here and now that weight training will not magically turn a non-effective art into an effective one. Only correct training in the correct manner will do that. What it will do is add to your response, both physically and mentally, strength, endurance and confidence. It stands to reason that a strong, trained muscle is going to be more effective in a combat scenario than a weak, untrained muscle.

Without wishing to go too much out of the context of weight training I think a little more detail is necessary. Here is a section from *Animal Day:*

'What is the correct training?' I hear you all saying. And for that matter, 'What is the correct art?' This is a sensitive area. So many people think that theirs is the complete art and that others are less, or not at all, effective. They think that they are open-minded and others are not, and that they have all the answers where others have only questions. Even the so-called 'new wave' martial artists who left tradition because of blinkered senior instructors and 'the classical mess', now wear their own blinkers and have, in a way, created their own classical mess.

As far as self-protection is concerned, every system has something to offer, and to say that it does not is to be blinkered. To trash all traditionalists, which seems very fashionable at the moment, simply because they are traditional, or to trash other stylists because they do not follow the same way as us would also be very blinkered. The one thing that all martial arts have in common is that we can all learn something from each other, if we'll only open our eyes wide enough to see.

Weight Training for the Martial Artist

Understanding your own art means little more than being honest, even if it is only with yourself.

Is your art a kicking art, punching art, or a grappling art? Is it close range, long range, semi-contact, full contact, an attacking art or a defensive art? Whatever your art is, analyse what it is not, and that will be where your weakness lies.

It is also important to analyse whether your main range, be it kicking, punching or grappling, is predominantly short range or long range. Are you a long range kicker or a short range kicker? Long range puncher or short range puncher? Whatever you are, again your weakness will lie in the range – within your main range – that you are weakest at.

Then what you have to ask yourself is: am I effective at my main range? Of course, everyone likes to think that they are, but mostly they are not. As an example, I would class you as a good puncher if you could do three rounds with a good boxer; I would consider you a good kicker if you could do three with a good Thai boxer or taekwon-do fighter; and I would certainly consider you good in close if you could go fifteen minutes with a good wrestler or judoka.

As a young karataka I was predominantly a kicker, but thought myself a good puncher too. I'd worked on the weights all my life and touched grappling so also thought my groundwork to be competent. When I tried to place my skills in the real world of fighting I quickly realised that my main range, kicking, was immediately neutralised by my environment. Most fights start at conversation range, this being punching range, so there was no room to kick in 95 per cent of all situations. If there was room it was quickly gobbled up by a greedy aggressor who wanted to be in my face.

I was a strong puncher; I could hit the bag hard, but basically I was a long range, straight puncher and conditioned to pull my blows on impact 90 per cent of the time. Real fighting is very close range and often demands the better suited hook or uppercut, but they weren't on my curriculum. The first time I hit someone I automatically pulled the punch on impact. I also felt out of range, a range that seemed to disappear before my eyes and wouldn't stay still for a second.

The first time I went to grappling range in the street I didn't have a clue what to do. I bludgeoned my way through and made a hard and long job out of something that should have been clinical. I was also completely unaccustomed to raw aggression and didn't know how to react to verbal. People were throwing verbal attacks and I didn't know how to defend, counter attack or even simply attack.

Ninety per cent of what goes into a real fight is not in the physical, it is in the psychological: openers, weakeners, primers and even finishing blows are secured with dialogue, the attacker using verbal missiles to attack the psyche. All I knew, all my art had taught me, was the physical response; a little like teaching someone how to dive in the swimming pool but not teaching him how to swim. It is true that fighting arts teach you distancing and timing, but the distancing in the street is different from that of the dojo. So is the timing, because you are fighting at a different range; it is different because it is enforced by the enemy and the environment.

So be realistic when evaluating your art: if you think that your art is good, test it. Not just at the strongest end but also at the weakest end, where the leaks are, then set about sealing up those leaks. As they say, 'a chain is only as strong as its weakest link'.

One of the main weaknesses that I have found in the arts that I have studied, and I have studied most of them, is that they all, with the exception of western boxing, condition their practitioners to fight defensively, certainly when they teach the self-defence aspect of the art. They teach their practitioners to wait for the attacker to attack, then block and counter attack. In the real world? Too late! Too late by a long shot. It doesn't take much logic to realise that action is quicker than reaction.

Now down to the nitty-gritty of what weight training can do for you and your art. I will go through a list of some of the arts and state which muscles are predominantly used and in what way. If your art is not listed then fit yourself into either the kick-punch category or the grapple-throw category, if your art involves all ranges then all of the following will apply.

It is fair to say that all muscles are used in *all* arts in some way or another, though certain muscles and muscle groups are used more than others. The art heading is also inclusive of most styles within that main group.

KARATE

Karate is predominantly a kicking and punching art, leaning more to the kicking than the punching. The major muscle groups used in karate are: hips (kicking), thighs (kicking and stance work), calves (kicking and stance work), abdominals (turning the upper body and taking blows), inner pectorals (punching and blocking movements), front deltoids (blocking and punching) and triceps (punching and some blocking).

GUNG-FU

Gung-fu, like karate, is best known for its kicking and punching skills, though often at a closer range than karate. It too leans more to kicking than punching. The major muscle groups used in gung-fu are: hips (kicking), thighs (kicking and stance work), calves (kicking and stance work), abdominals (turning the upper body and taking blows), inner pectorals (punching and blocking movements), front deltoids (blocking and punching) and triceps (punching and some blocking).

WESTERN BOXING

Western boxing is purely a punching and blocking art, though often at varying ranges. The major muscle groups used in boxing are: thighs (for footwork and stance work), calves (for footwork and stance work), abdominals (turning the upper body and taking blows), inner pectorals (punching and blocking movements), front deltoids (blocking and punching), triceps (punching and some blocking), trapezius (for supporting the neck against heavy blows).

THAI-BOXING

Thai is one of the most demanding and ferocious of the fighting arts and covers nearly all ranges, lacking only in ground fighting and, to a degree, vertical grappling. The major muscle groups used in Thai boxing are: thighs (for footwork and stance work and absorbing leg kicks), calves (for footwork and stance work), tibialis and extensor hullucus (shins – for blocking leg kicks), abdominals (turning the upper body and taking blows), inner pectorals (punching and blocking movements), front deltoids (blocking and punching), triceps (punching and some blocking), trapezius (for supporting the neck against heavy blows), biceps and forearms (for punch retraction and gripping), upper back (for hugging and pulling).

JU-JITSU

Some styles of ju-jitsu actually do cover all ranges. The major muscle groups used are: thighs (for stance work and some kicking), hips (for throwing and some kicking), calves (footwork and stance work and lifting the body onto the toes for throwing), abdominals (turning the upper body and taking blows), inner pectorals (punching and blocking movements), front deltoids (blocking and punching), triceps (punching and some blocking), biceps and forearms (for punch retraction and gripping), upper back (for hugging and pulling).

WRESTLING AND JUDO

Judo and wrestling are limited to the grappling ranges, vertical and horizontal. As far as contact go they are totally real and often ferocious. The major muscle groups used are: thighs (for stance work and some leg chokes/strangles), hips (for throwing), calves (footwork and stance work and lifting the body onto the toes for throwing), abdominals (turning the upper body, taking blows and lifting the body in escapes), front deltoids (for jamming techniques), biceps and forearms (gripping/holding), upper back (for hugging and pulling), trapezius (for protecting the neck and throat from strangles and chokes).

AIKIDO

Aikido works on the premise that you use your opponent's strength and weight against them and that muscular strength is not used in the execution of technique, so I would recommend that the practitioner use weight for overall muscle strengthening covering all major muscle groups. I would also recommend that they read *Animal Day* for reasons that will be evident when the book is read.

CHAPTER FOUR
SAFETY FIRST

As with all aspects of training, safety is an important aspect, weight training being no different. Safety should be paramount at all times if accidents and injuries are to be avoided.

WARMING UP

Always warm up the muscles before engaging in a weight training session. Cold muscles are easily pulled and ripped (see next chapter on 'warm ups').

USING A SPOT (Training Partner)

A training partner, or spot, should be used when lifting, or training with weights, especially when using heavy weights. The training partner should 'spot' during the execution of an exercise and when necessary they should lift the weight on and off the bench press or rack for you and assist during the exercise if you are struggling to lift the weight. A spot is also good for offering encouragement during the exercise.

DRESSING CORRECTLY

Always wear loose fitting clothes that allow for muscle expansion when training with the weights. Men's tight trousers and underpants are especially uncomfortable, even dangerous. They should be like a good dancing hall, 'loads of ball room'. Sturdy trainers with good floor grip are also important. Don't wear jewellery and make sure that long hair is tied up so that it cannot get caught in machinery in the gym. If and when necessary use a weightlifter's belt to support the back.

SECURING EQUIPMENT

Use collars to secure weights to the bar and dumb-bells so that they cannot fall on you, or anyone else, during the execution of the exercise. One of the most common accidents in the weights gym is weight discs falling from unsecured bar or dumb-bells on to toes. So beware and always secure the weights with collars.

SLOWLY DOES IT

From my experience people, especially those who train in other disciplines such as the martial arts, tend to rush into weight training in a bid to show how fit they are and to get fast gains in strength and lift. This is always a mistake. Take your time and start off with light weights and manageable routines. Don't be influenced by the weight and routine of those around you, or your own ego; it is not a race or a competition.

Just do what is comfortable to start with and nothing more. Gently increase your weight week by week and month by month and if needed, your routine. If you do try to do too much at once it is possible that you may rip or damage the muscle and this will kill your appetite for weight training. Too much too soon will also leave you so sore that you will not be able to move, let alone train. All these things will defeat the object because it will affect the way you train in the combat system that you are trying to enhance.

WARM DOWN

To help lessen the chance of aching muscles, due to lactic acid left in the muscle after training, warm down with the exercises described at the end of this book.

CHAPTER FIVE
WARMING UP

You will be tempted to miss the warm up when you enter the gym, I always am. Don't do it. *Always* warm up the muscles so that they are ready for the trauma of a training session. Most injuries in training are caused by people who do not warm up. If you get into the habit of warming up it will become routine.

A good warm up will get the heart and lungs working to their optimum level aerobically, thoroughly warming up the body so that you do not strain any muscles. The following exercises will do the job admirably.

The warm up should consist of two parts:

1) Stretching
To lengthen your muscles, tendons and ligaments as much as possible to produce maximum flexibility.

2) High Repetition
Aerobic exercise to get the heart and lungs working to increase the blood supply to the muscles.

When I warm up I try to work from the head down to the toes, so we will start with the neck.

1) NECK ROLLS

The neck and the shoulders are the repository of a lot of the body's tensions, so neck rolls are the first step toward physical relaxation. I find neck rolls especially important if you are going to practice any type of grappling discipline where the neck takes a lot of the strain.

Stand with your hands by your sides and breathe deeply, letting your shoulders, arms and whole body relax as much as possible. Let your head fall forward slowly until your chin touches your chest. This will gently stretch the back of the neck. Then rotate the head to your right and all the way around as though trying to get your right ear to touch your right shoulder. After completion of one rep do another four. Five reps in all. (Pic 9)

9

2) SIDE BENDS

This movement stretches the side of the body, especially the oblique muscles. Place your left arm by your left side and your right arm above your head, your legs shoulder width apart and straight (as illustrated). Bend to your left side and stretch gently, not bouncing, as far as you can comfortably go. At full stretch hold for the count of five seconds and then return slowly to the start position. Repeat for ten reps and then do the same to the opposite side of the body. (Pic 10)

3) TOUCHING THE TOES

This will stretch the back and the back leg muscles. Stand with feet shoulder width apart, hands in front and palms facing inward. Bend forward, trying to touch your fingertips on the floor without bending the legs. At full stretch hold for five seconds. Again, don't bounce, rather stretch gently. Return to start position and repeat for ten reps. (Pic 11)

4) HAMSTRING STRETCH

Stand with legs twice shoulder width and lean forward until the palms of the hands are on the floor in front of you. Turn to your left, grab your left ankle and hold for five seconds. Turn to the right side and repeat the same exercise to the right side, holding at full stretch for five seconds. Then return

back to the centre and repeat the
same for ten reps each side. As with
all stretching, do not bounce.
(Pic 12)

5) BACK STRETCH

Standing with the hands on the hips,
feet shoulder width apart, lean the
head back as though looking at the
ceiling above you and gently stretch
backwards, as though trying to look
at the wall behind you. At full stretch
hold for five seconds and return to
start position. Repeat the same
movement for ten reps, each time
trying to stretch a little further than
the last.
(Pic 13)

6) INNER AND REVERSE THIGH STRETCH

From a squat position, back straight (as illustrated), extend your right leg to your right. Use your right hand to gently push your right knee towards the floor, thus stretching the inner/back thigh and calf muscle. At the same time use your left elbow to push out against the inside of your left knee, thus stretching the inner thigh of the opposite leg. Repeat for ten reps. (Pic 14)

To reverse, return to the squat position and extend the opposite (left) leg. Each rep should see you stretching the muscle a little more. Do not bounce or force the muscle.

14

7) LEGS APART – SEATED HAMSTRING STRETCH

Sit on the floor, legs astride and straight. Gently lean down towards your right side, grabbing your right ankle or foot to pull down, then move to the centre and stretch forward, trying to place your head or chest on the floor in front of you.

Then move across to your left side and lean forward, taking hold of your left ankle or foot and pulling down gently.

Alternate the exercise from left to right to centre, each rep trying to stretch a little further than the last. Thirty reps in total. Don't bounce or jerk. (Pic 15)

15

8) BOX SPLITS

Stand with feet astride and legs straight. Slowly slide both feet in opposite directions and gently downwards. Keep your back straight. If you need to, place a chair or table in front of you to aid balance. When you reach your full stretch, hold for five seconds and then return to the start position. Repeat for ten reps. (Pic 16)

9) FRONT SPLITS

Facing your own right (left if practising the opposite side) legs astride with the hip committed to the right, both legs straight, slide the feet in opposite directions slowly and gently towards the front splits. When you reach your full potential hold the movement for five seconds and then return to the start position. Repeat for ten reps. Change to the left side and repeat the exercise. (Pic 17)

10) JOGGING ON THE SPOT

From a standing position begin running on the spot trying to lift each alternate knee as high as possible in front of you. Try to stay on the balls of the feet at all times during the exercise as landing on the heels may cause injury. As you continue to jog on the spot try to increase the speed and intensity of the exercise and try getting the knees higher and higher.

16

17

CHAPTER SIX
ROUTINE ONE
– KICKERS AND PUNCHERS

Routine One is more for the boxer/karate/tae-kwondo fighter, the punchers and kickers of the fighting arts, whereas Routine Two will be better suited to the grappling arts. If your art involves all ranges, and it should, then you could use both of the following routines, or a combination of the two.

I find it best to train two or three times a week on the weights, but never on consecutive days; this allows the worked muscle recuperation time.

Always do a five to ten minute warm up, as described in the last chapter, before lifting any weight, and warm down after finishing your session.

As a rule of thumb, use a weight that will allow 6-8 reps, building eventually to 12-15 reps. When you find that you are achieving 12-15 reps, add a little more weight to the bar and come back down to 6-8 reps. Follow all the normal safety procedures: keep collars tight, have a spot for any exercise that might be a struggle and above all, *don't strain yourself.*

18a

Note that correct breathing is important when using the weights. Try to breathe in when the muscle extends and out when the muscle flexes.

The major muscle groups used in this routine are: hips, calves, abdominal muscles, inner pectorals, front deltoids (shoulders) and triceps.

18b

1) 5-10 minute warm up.

2) CLEAN AND PRESS

A full clean, then press over the head is one rep. Put the bar down on the floor after every clean and press. Main muscles worked: legs, back, trapezius, deltoids, triceps. (Pic 18a,b&c)

18c

Weight Training for the Martial Artist

A clean is performed by standing close to the bar-bell, as illustrated, with the shins just about touching the bar. Grab the bar at about shoulder width and lift the bar by pushing with the legs as you pull with the arms. When the bar reaches shoulder height, flip the wrists over, so that the bar is resting across the upper chest at the level of the collarbones. From this position 'press' the bar over your head strongly, fully locking the elbows. Lower the weight back to the chest position and then back to the original start position, on the floor. Repeat the clean and press for 6-8 reps almost immediately.

Perform three sets of clean and press with one minute rest between sets (one set is the amount of reps performed in one go, usually between 6 and 15 repetitions of the movement).

Add a couple of reps a workout until you are achieving 12-15 reps per set, then add a little weight and drop back down to three sets of 6-8 reps.

3) FORTY-FIVE DEGREE INCLINE DUMB-BELL PRESS

Main muscles worked: upper and inner pectorals, front deltoids and triceps.

Lying on your back on an incline bench, a dumb-bell in each hand at upper chest/shoulder level, push the weights overhead then lower back to the start position on the chest/shoulders for one rep. Repeat the movement for three sets of 6-8 reps, increasing a few reps workout until you achieve 12-15 reps, then add weight and drop back down to 6-8 reps.

(Pic 19a&b)

4) LUNGES

Main muscles worked: hips, thighs and calves.

Holding a dumb-bell in each hand, hanging at the sides of the body, take a long step forward with one foot, lowering the knee of the back leg, and bending the knee of the front leg. Come back to the starting position and repeat the movement with the opposite leg. This double step is one rep. (Pic 20a)

Repeat for three sets of 6-8 reps increasing over several workouts to 12-15 reps. When this is achieved add weight and decrease the reps back down to 6-8. (Pic 20b)

5) ALTERNATE DUMB-BELL CURL

Main muscles worked: biceps, forearms.

Stand with a dumb-bell in each hand, with the thumb end forward. Curl one hand to the shoulder turning the dumb-bell en route so that the palm side is upward. Return the dumb-bell to its start position at the same time as you begin to curl the opposite hand in the same manner. Both dumb-bells should meet at about halfway. This is one rep. Continue, alternating up and down, until you complete 6-8 reps for each arm. (Pic 21)

Repeat for three sets of 6-8 reps increasing over several workouts to 12-15 reps. When this is achieved add weight and decrease the reps back down to 6-8 reps.

6) TRICEPS DIPS

Main muscles worked: triceps, shoulders and chest (a little).

For this exercise you need three chairs, boxes, benches or something similar. Place your heels on one of the boxes and your hands on the other two, as per illustration. You should be in a position similar to sitting on the floor with the legs straight out in front of you. Lower your bum as far as you can, then push back to the start position with the strength of the triceps. This is one rep. (Pic 22&23)

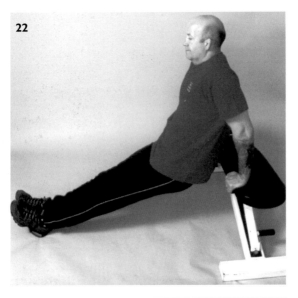

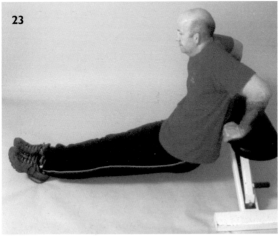

Repeat for three sets of 6-8 reps, increasing over several workouts to 12-15 reps. When this is achieved, add weight and decrease the reps back down to 6-8 reps.

There are two ways of adding resistance to this exercise:

1) Have someone place a loose weight (disc) on your lap. This can be increased as the exercise becomes easier.

2) As you push back up from the flexed position, get someone to place a little pressure on your shoulders to add to the resistance.

ABDOMINALS

Main muscles worked: abdominals/obliques.

To the bodybuilder the abs are for show; for the martial artist their use is threefold: for mobility, for support and for impact; being able to take a shot in the stomach. So on the abs we will do three exercises.

1) KNEE BENT TWISTING SIT-UPS

Anchor your feet, bend your knees and place your hands on your head, as illustrated. Sit up and touch your right knee with your left elbow, then lower to start position. This is one rep. Repeat the sit-up again, this time touching your left knee with

23a

your right elbow. Work up to two sets of fifty repetitions, then either increase resistance by doing the same exercise on an incline or by holding a weight behind your head, or on your chest as you sit up. (Pic 23a)

2) SEATED KNEE-INS

Sit on the edge of a chair or a bench, hold the side of the chair for support, with feet together, as illustrated. From this position pull the knees to the chest and then lower to the start position for one rep. Repeat the movement and work up to two sets of 50 reps. (Pic 24)

24

3) IMPACT

Lie on your back on the floor, bend the knees and lift the shoulders off the floor, enough to tense the abs. Get a partner to gently tap your belly with clenched fists. Be sure to start off gently.

Continue for 10-20 seconds. Slowly increase both the time and degree of impact until you can take one minute, with medium force.

TAKE CARE
NOTE: Professional boxers do this by dropping a medicine ball onto their tensed abs.

CAUTION: never strike a relaxed stomach.

This is the complete routine, the only thing that I'd recommend you add is neck work. The next routine, the grappler's workout, includes neck work and you could greatly benefit by its inclusion in your routine.

CHAPTER SEVEN
ROUTINE TWO
– THE GRAPPLERS

Routine One was more for the boxer/karate/tae-kwondo fighter, the kickers and punchers of the fighting arts, whereas Routine Two is more suited to the grappling arts. As previously stated, if your art involves all ranges as it should, then you could use both routines, or a combination of the two.

As a practising grappler I have found this routine to be of the utmost benefit. It has greatly enhanced my grappling skills, not just with added strength to aid technique but also with extra stamina. Always do a five to ten minute warm up, as described in Chapter Five, before lifting any weight, and warm down after finishing your session.

As a rule of thumb, use a weight that will allow 6-8 reps, building eventually to 12-15 reps. When you find that you are achieving 12-15 reps, add a little more weight to the bar and come back down to 6-8 reps. Follow all the normal safety procedures: keep collars tight, have a spot for any exercise that might be a struggle and above all don't strain yourself.

The major muscle groups used in this routine are: biceps, upper-back, forearms, hips, thighs and shoulders.

1) 5-10 minute warm-up.

2) WIDE STANCE SQUATS

Main muscles used: thighs, hips, gripping muscles.

Hold a pair of heavy dumb-bells and stand with feet about 18 inches to 2 feet apart. Squat down until the dumb-bells touch the floor, then return to the start position. This is one rep. Repeat for three sets of 12 reps, eventually working up to three sets of 20 reps. When this is achieved, increase the weight and drop the reps back down to 12. (Pic 25a&b)

25a

25b

3) WIDE GRIP BENCH PRESS

Main muscles used: pectorals, front shoulders, triceps.

Lie on your back on a bench and hold the bar-bell 'collar-to-collar', as per illustration. Lower the bar to your chest and then push back to arm's length, the start position. This is one rep. Repeat the exercise for three sets of 12 reps building up to three sets of 20 reps, increasing the weight and lowering the reps, as previously described. (Pic 26a&b)

4) POWER CLEANS

Main muscles used: all upper back, hips, grip, lats.

Use a fairly heavy bar, grip it at shoulder width, shins touching the bar, as per illustration. Pull the bar fast from the floor, flipping the bar onto the front shoulders (collarbone level) as you come upright. Lower back to the start position. This is one rep. Repeat the movement at a fairly fast pace for three sets of 6-8 reps working up to three sets of 12-15 reps, increasing poundage and decreasing reps accordingly. (Pic 27a&b)

27a

27b

5) BAR-BELL CURLS – BASIC AND HEAVY

Main muscles used: biceps and forearms for grip.

28a

Curl the bar at shoulder width grip from the thighs to the chest and back down again. This is one rep. Use a 'loose' style with a bit of body swing on the last couple of reps, if needed. Repeat for five sets of 8 reps, building to five sets of 15 reps, increasing poundage and decreasing reps accordingly. (Pic 28a&b)

28b

6) ALTERNATE DUMB-BELL PRESS – STANDING OR SEATED

Main muscles used: deltoids, triceps.

29a

Hold a dumb-bell in each hand at shoulder height, as per illustration. Push the dumb-bells over the head alternately (one at a time) getting a nice rhythm going. Up and down with both arms being one rep. Repeat for three sets of 12 reps building to three sets of 20 reps, increasing poundage and decreasing reps accordingly. (Pic 29a&b)

29b

7) TWO-MINUTE NECK WORK

Main muscle worked: neck.

Use your hands to provide gentle resistance as you twist and turn your head in all directions. Be careful though; it is very easy to pull the neck muscles. This is achieved in the same way as rolling the head, as in the warm up, using your hands to apply a little pressure to the exercise.

8) HEAD CRAB

Main muscles used: neck and trapezius.

Lie on your back on the ground and make a crab position. Lower your head until it is resting on the mat, as per illustration, still using the hands for support. Gently rock back and forward and side to side, on the head. Use the hands to keep some of the bodyweight off the head. As the neck becomes stronger, use the hands less and less until you are performing the exercise without any support from the hands at all.

(Pic 30)

This is a very difficult exercise and should be practised with great caution. Neck muscles are easy to pull so be *careful*. This exercise is of five minutes duration.

9) ABDOMINALS
Main muscle used: abs.

For the martial artist, stomach muscles are not for show; their use is for more practical reasons – for mobility, support and impact, being able to take a shot in the stomach. So for the abs we will do three exercises.

(i) KNEE BENT TWISTING SIT-UPS
Anchor your feet, bend your knees and place your hands on your head, as per illustration. Sit up and touch your right knee with your left elbow, lower to start position. This is one rep. Repeat the sit-up again, this time touching your left knee with your right elbow. Work up to two sets of 50 repetitions, then either increase resistance by doing the same exercise on an incline or by holding a weight behind your head, or on your chest as you sit up.

(ii) SEATED KNEE-INS

Sit on the edge of a chair or a bench, holding the sides for support and with feet together, as illustrated. From this position pull the knees to the chest and lower to the start position for one rep. Repeat the movement and work up to two sets of 50 reps.

(iii) IMPACT

Lie on your back on the floor, bend the knees and lift the shoulders off the floor, enough to tense the abs. Get a partner to tap your belly gently with clenched fists.

Continue for 10-20 seconds. Slowly increase both the time and degree of impact until you can take one minute, with medium force.

Remember: never strike a relaxed stomach.

This is the end of Routine Two. As I said before, if you intend your art to be an effective one in a street scenario it should include all ranges and all concepts. Every system should include kicking, punching and grappling ranges. If it doesn't, it cannot be classed as a comprehensive or completely effective system.

In my opinion and contrary to popular belief, there isn't a system that is so effective in its main range that it does not need to practice other ranges. Many practitioners say that their system of kicking and striking is so effective that they don't need to learn the grappling range because they will never end up on the floor. With respect, that is, at best, naïve. What I am trying to say here, in a rather long-winded manner, is that if you do include all ranges within your system, then use both routines, or a combination of the exercises in the two.

Also worth a mention is the fact that there are a myriad of exercises besides these that can be used to train the major muscles related to your art; you don't just have to do the ones here. What I do recommend though, is that you use these routines until you become very familiar with the weights, then, if you want to change the exercises, reps, sets or routines, by all means do so. Variety is the spice of life as they say. Try, though, not to detract from the main aim of weights for the martial artist: you are not training for a beach physique, or a weight or power lifting contest. Weight training is an addition.

Treat the gym as a place of learning; study those around you and the exercises that they are practising. You may find as you train in the weights' gym, that others are working on different exercises to you. Make a mental note of these exercises and their functions (ask the instructor or even the other people in the gym if you are not sure) and, if and when you are ready, include them in your own routine, or replace some of your own exercises with the new ones. Make sure though that they relate to your art, otherwise you will be defeating the object.

If you are ever unsure of what you are doing, or you need advice, ask the resident gym instructor.

CHAPTER EIGHT
RÉSUMÉ

Here is a résumé of the two routines.

ROUTINE ONE:
KICKERS AND PUNCHERS

1) **WARM UP:**
   5-10 minutes.

2) **CLEAN AND PRESS:**
   Three sets of 6-8 reps to three sets of 12-15 reps.

3) **INCLINE DUMB-BELL PRESS:**
   Three sets of 6-8 reps to three sets of 12-15 reps.

4) **LUNGES:**
   Three sets of 6-8 reps to three sets of 12-15 reps each leg.

5) **ALTERNATE DUMB-BELL CURLS:**
   Three sets of 6-8 reps to three sets of 12-15 reps.

6) **TRICEPS DIPS:**
   Three sets of 6-8 reps to three sets of 12-15 reps.

7) **TWISTING SIT-UPS:**
   Two sets of up to 50 reps.

8) SEATED KNEE-INS:
Two sets of up to 50 reps.

9) IMPACT TRAINING:
Ten seconds to one minute of light to medium impact.

10) WARM DOWN:
(Detailed in later chapter).

ROUTINE TWO: THE GRAPPLERS

1) WARM UP:
5-10 minutes.

2) DUMB-BELL SQUATS:
Three sets of 12 reps to three sets of 20 reps.

3) WIDE GRIP BENCH PRESS:
Three sets of 12 reps to three sets of 20 reps.

4) POWER CLEANS:
Three sets of 6-8 reps to three sets of 12-15 reps.

5) BAR-BELL CURLS:
Five sets of 8 reps to five sets of 15 reps.

6) ALTERNATE DUMB-BELL PRESS:
Three sets of 12 reps to three sets of 20 reps.

7)   NECK WORK:
Two minutes.

8)   HEAD CRABS:
Up to five minutes.

9)   TWISTING SIT UPS:
Two sets of up to 50 reps.

10) SEATED KNEE-INS:
Two sets of up to 50 reps.

11) IMPACT TRAINING:
Ten seconds to one minute of light to medium impact.

12) WARM DOWN:
(Detailed in later chapter).

CHAPTER NINE
WARMING DOWN

The following exercises should be performed directly after finishing on the weights, whilst the muscles are still warm and pumped. This will help stretch the muscles for flexibility, get rid of any lactic acid remaining in the muscle after exertion and also act as a relaxing aid. Warming down should be gentle and therefore therapeutic after a hard workout.

I) HAMSTRING STRETCHES

Stand with the feet together and legs locked straight. Bend forward from the waist. Grab hold of your ankles (or simply touch your toes) and gently pull down to your maximum stretch. Hold for a couple of seconds and then return to the start position. One set of ten reps. (Pic 33)

33

2) LEGS APART – HAMSTRING STRETCHES

Sit on the floor, legs astride and straight. Gently lean down toward your right side, grabbing your right ankle or foot to pull down, then move to the centre and stretch forward, trying to place your head or chest on the floor in front of you. Then move across to your left side and lean forward, taking hold of your left ankle or foot and pull down gently. (Pic 34)

34

Alternate the exercise from left to right to centre, each rep trying to stretch a little further than the last. Don't bounce or jerk. Ten reps each side and centre.

3) INNER THIGH STRETCHES

Sit on the floor and draw your legs together so that the soles of the feet touch. Hold on to your feet and lower your knees to either side as far as you can. Use your arms or elbows to place gentle pressure on your legs and so get the fullest possible stretch. At maximum stretch hold for five seconds then release. Repeat the exercise for ten reps. (Pic 35)

35

4) QUAD STRETCH

From a kneeling position sit back gently between your own ankles, as illustrated, then lie back as far as you can. At full stretch hold for 3-5 seconds and then return to the start position and repeat the exercise for ten reps, each time trying to stretch a little further than the last. (Pic 36)

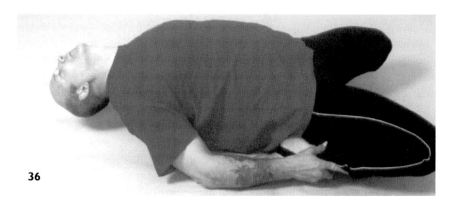

36

5) HURDLE STRETCH

Sit in the hurdle position, as illustrated, and gently stretch forward, grabbing the right ankle or foot (left if sitting the opposite way) and pull gently forward. Then lean over to your left and stretch between your legs, then to your right and stretch to your rear leg. Repeat front, centre and rear for ten reps each, trying gently to stretch a little deeper with each subsequent rep. (Pic 37)

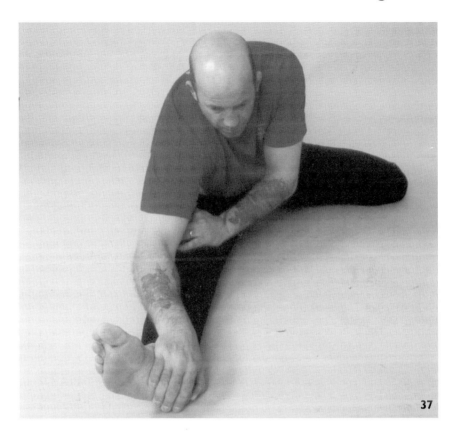

37

6) SHAKING IT OFF

From a standing position, gently shake all of the limbs in turn from the head to the ankles.

CHAPTER TEN
THINGS TO AVOID

As with all endeavours there are things to remember and there are things to avoid. The next two chapters are dedicated to these tangible and intangible points.

1) A lot of martial arts types use punching with weights as an exercise, believing it to increase punching power, such as punching with dumb-bells. It doesn't because:

• The main upper body muscles used in correct punching are oblique muscles, abdominals, pectorals and triceps. The anterior (front) deltoids are only used in a very minor way.

• When you punch with a weight, gravity tries to pull the weight down to the floor. This isn't in the line of the resistance used in punching technique.

• So punching with a weight is not to be advised because it will develop the wrong muscles.

2) Try not to overdevelop the latissimus dorsi (lats) and certainly do not become a 'lat spreader'; you'll have seen this pose in the muscle magazines and bodybuilding contests. It may look great on stage but it pushes the arms away from the sides of your body in an unnatural manner and this limits certain combative movement.

3) When training the thighs by doing leg presses, squats etc., try to keep the reps high as opposed to low, up to 20 reps. Martial artists use both dynamic (moving strength) and static power (stances). Heavy quads, as brought on by heavy leg training with low reps, may interfere with mobility.

4) Keep your weight training in context. The weights have a habit of seducing people away from their main aim, in this case, aiding our combat training. They become obsessed with size, strength and physique and the weight training becomes more important to them than the combat art that they are training in.

I have lost count of the number of people I know personally who have gone in to weight training for added strength or bodyweight and have become seduced, packing in their combat art in a bid to get big. Some, probably most, see big as synonymous with hard. Let me tell you that big is not in the biceps, it is in the mind. This is not to decry people that train with weights, I have a lot of admiration for anyone that trains, full stop, it is just to say that MASSIVE is a mental concept and not a physical one, so don't be seduced.

As a matter of fact, all the people that I know, with one exception, that left the martial arts for the weights, returned later when they realised the truth in what I have just said.

5) Don't become a 'water boy'. That is, don't take banned substances. There is obviously a lot of politics about the use of steroids and I don't want to go into that now. Only to say that steroids are detrimental to good health and people are dying through the misuse of them. Steroids are a banned substance from sport. If you use them you are cheating not only your art but also your body, and worst of all yourself. You can make excuses all day long about how steroids 'are all right in moderation' and how you are only going to take one course but at the end of the day they are unhealthy, so don't be a fool or a cheat. Stay natural. What we are training for is health; anything that detracts from that should be bypassed.

6) Don't become overconfident. I don't like to say it but, whilst training with the weights does develop confidence, this being a good thing, it is also a breeding ground for arrogance, a by-product of overconfidence. Confidence and overconfidence are but a hair width apart. Overconfidence is a negative by-product, sometimes of the weights but moreover of the steroids. Look out for it lest it creep up on you whilst you are unawares. Get strong – stay respectful.

CHAPTER ELEVEN
THINGS TO REMEMBER

1) It is quite difficult to be a top combat man and a top bodybuilder at the same time. When you talk about this combination people often bring up the name Terry O'Neill because he seems to combine them very well. Although Terry has a terrific physique, it is only for the last four or five years that he has been physique orientated. At about three stone bodyweight lighter Terry fought and beat the world's best in karate and the world's worst in society.

2) The super cuts of the bodybuilder reduce the body's impact ability. A little fat covering the body can provide cushioning against heavy blows, not enough to flap and wobble, but perhaps half a stone (7lb) spread over the whole of the body has many benefits.

3) A 20-inch arm is not necessarily any stronger than a 17-inch arm, neither is there a guarantee that it will punch any harder. Rocky Marciano's arms were 16.5 inches and as we all know he could punch a bit. Most of the power in a punch (or a kick) comes from how the technique is delivered as

opposed to how big the limb is. Some of the strongest punchers that I have ever worked with only weighed 9-10 stone with very small bicep measurements.

4) A lot of the top, pro boxers do not have showy abs and they take punches to the body all day long. As I said before, a cut stomach is not always the sign of a strong stomach.

5) If you don't train hard, don't expect to get results. Many people go to the gym and wander from exercise to exercise without breaking into a sweat, then after 12 months they complain that the weights haven't done anything for them. That's because they haven't done any real training. If you work hard you'll get the results; it's as simple as that.

CHAPTER TWELVE
DIET

Diet is not just an important part of training with the weights, it is an important part of any training regime.

You are only as good as the food you eat and if you want the best out of your body then it stands to reason that you should put the best into it. It has never ceased to amaze me in my years of training, the amount of people that do not follow a good diet and then wonder why they get no results, are always tired and run down. Probably as much as 75 per cent of training is in the diet, and yet people still neglect it.

I know what food works for me and what food does not, but diet is not my specialised subject so I will not go into great detail here, only to tell you what food the body needs. Personal needs vary also: you may want to lose weight, gain weight, lose fat, gain muscle or just add healthy bodyweight. You may have a fast metabolic rate, you may have a slow metabolic rate, and you probably have a preference for certain types of food. Some foods will perhaps not respond for you as they would for others and vice-versa. There are many variables that need specialised attention. I recommend that you see a dietician about what food is best for you and what you want to achieve.

The main aims of a healthy diet are to reduce your fat and sugar intake. That means cutting right down on: fried foods, cream, butter, red meat, chocolate, cakes, biscuits, pastries, sweetened fruit juices, fizzy drinks and sweets. Increase all the foods with low fat, high carbohydrates, protein and fibre: chicken, oily fish, milk, fresh fruit, vegetables, beans, brown rice, wholemeal bread and pasta. Try to keep your alcohol intake down to the recommended 14 units a week for women, and 21 for men.

The basic ingredients in a good health diet should include:

PROTEIN

Protein is essential for the repair of muscle tissue which is torn or broken down in every training session. The whole body is made up of protein.

Protein can be found in most foods, specifically fish, chicken, meat and dairy products (eggs, cheese, milk etc.). Cheese has a high vitamin, mineral and protein content, and although a little high in fat, helps to provide high energy levels.

FIBRE

Beans and bran provide the fibre needed in a healthy diet, and also help to prevent the digestive system becoming sluggish.

CARBOHYDRATE

Carbs are the body's first choice fuel, needed for the essential energy of a training session and everyday living. Carbs are abundant in fruit, pasta, baked potatoes and rice. I especially find bananas an excellent source of carbs.

VITAMINS AND MINERALS

Vitamins and minerals are pivotal in the breaking down of protein, carbs and calories into the system for easy utilisation for the working body. If the food is not properly digested it cannot be used by the body and just leaves as waste.

Vitamins and minerals can be found in most health foods, especially fruit and vegetables. Vitamin and mineral supplements are also excellent back-ups.

CALORIES

Calories are needed for the maintenance of bodyweight and also act as a secondary fuel to carbs. They can be found in almost everything that you eat, in varying degrees. Calorie intake can be adjusted to alter bodyweight, up or down.

Take my advice and be very conscientious about what you eat: you don't have to be a biochemist to eat healthily, just sensible. If you are not sure what is and is not healthy then take professional advice.

EPILOGUE

So there it is, another addition to your training routine. If you conscientiously adhere to the exercises you will add tremendous raw power to your technique, strength to your response, and a great muscular armour. Training with the weights will give you a tremendous feeling of wellbeing. It also gives a much needed change from normal routine. I have always used the weights, and God willing, I always will. They have helped me immeasurably and they can help you too.

As a result of training with the weights, as well as all the other benefits formerly mentioned, I have managed to avoid some serious injuries that would have surely occurred if my muscles had not been up to strength. There have also been times in my job as a nightclub doorman, when the raw strength developed by working with weights has pulled me through against difficult, often impossible odds.

One benefit often missed with the weights is the control of the inner opponent, the inner voice that feeds you with negative thoughts. To put yourself through the pain of a hard session on the weights you have to learn self-control, control over the inner opponent. It is the inner opponent, that negative voice of ill reason at the back of our minds, that stops most people achieving their goals in life. So more control, via the weights, over the inner opponent has got to be a good thing.

Last, but not least, a nice by-product of working in progressive training is a good looking physique. It endears you to others and helps tremendously with increasing your self-esteem. Confident people are successful people, just beware and do not let that healthy confidence spill over into arrogant overconfidence.

I sincerely believe that you can make anything you want from your life, you can live your dreams. Whatever the mind of man can conceive he can achieve, so whatever it is that you want from life, go and get it. This is not a rehearsal, we have but one chance and we have absolutely no idea how long that chance is going to last. It could all end tomorrow, so make the best of today and live now. Use weight and combat training to help you achieve those very attainable goals.

God bless.

Geoff Thompson
Coventry England 2001

THE ELEPHANT AND THE TWIG

The Art Of
Positive Thinking

14 Golden Rules to Success and Happiness

GEOFF THOMPSON

author of *Watch My Back* and *Fear*

SUMMERSDALE

GEOFF THOMPSON

WATCH MY BACK

'I train for the first shot
– it's all I need.'

'LENNIE MCLEAN HAD THE BRAWN, DAVE COURTNEY HAD THE CHARM, BUT GEOFF THOMPSON IS IN A CLASS OF HIS OWN.' FHM

www.geoffthompson.com

www.summersdale.com